GIRLS ROCK!
Contents

KT-467-763

Jules   Rosa

CHAPTER 1

Great Idea

One hot, sunny morning, best friends Jules and Rosa are in the back garden at Jules's house. They lie side by side in a striped hammock tied between two trees.

Rosa "What did you think was the best part?"

Jules "Best part of what?"

Rosa "The circus, of course. What did you like the most?"

Jules "Oh, the ladies riding on horseback. I'm going to try that next time I go riding."

Jules smiles as she imagines herself, standing up on the back of a horse galloping around the centre ring of the circus.

Rosa "Yeah, right. I'm sure your mum is going to let you stand up on the back of a horse."

Jules "She can't stop me when I'm grown up. That's what I'm going to do for a job—ride horses in the circus!"

Rosa "I thought you were going to be a singer. La, la, la!"

Jules "I'm going to do both."

Rosa "A singing horseback rider? Hmmmm …"

Jules "So what did you like best?"

Rosa "The Flying Corsalinis. Remember them?"

Rosa pops out of the hammock, causing Jules to almost fall on the ground. Rosa starts jumping around with her arms stretched out in front of her. Jules stares at her.

Jules "Huh? Corsalinis? Ro, you're acting a bit weird."

Rosa "Remember the Flying Corsalinis? A whole family flying around on a trapeze all day!"

Jules "Oh, yeah. They were amazing."

Rosa "Remember when that girl jumped off the little platform and caught the trapeze bar? That's what I'm doing. I want to swing on a trapeze like that."

Jules rolls her eyes and catches sight of a branch above their head.

Jules "You can."

Rosa "I can what?"

Jules "Swing on a trapeze. I have a great idea."

CHAPTER 2

Tool Time

Jules gives Rosa a mysterious look.

Rosa "Swing on a trapeze. How?"
Jules "Look up there."

Jules points up.

Rosa "Okay, I see a branch. So what?"

Jules "We can build a trapeze and swing from there."

Rosa looks at her friend, and then the branch.

Jules "It's easy. All we need is a stick and some rope."

Rosa "Really? Oh, that's a great
   idea. I wish I'd thought of it."
Jules "Come on, then. We can find
   the stuff we need in the shed."

   Jules leads Rosa into a small
shed where her mum and dad keep
gardening tools and old junk.

Jules "Here's some rope."

Rosa "It's a bit thin, isn't it?"

Jules "It's my old skipping-rope. It's super-strong. It'll be fine. Look for a stick."

Rosa grabs an old broom.

Rosa "Here. This'll work for the bar."

Jules "With those bristles? There's got to be something better."

Rosa "It's perfect! We just need to cut off the broom part. Do you have a saw?"

Jules "A saw? My dad will flip if he sees me using his saw."

Rosa "Okay. Then we'll just have to use it with the bristles. It'll work."

Jules "If you say so. But first, let's cut the rope in half. I'll hold it while you cut with Mum's hedge clippers."

Rosa cuts the rope while Jules holds it.

Rosa "Now we have to tie the rope to the bar."

Jules "Yeah. We need super-knots! I know exactly what to do … well, I think I know what to do. I have to practise. Follow me."

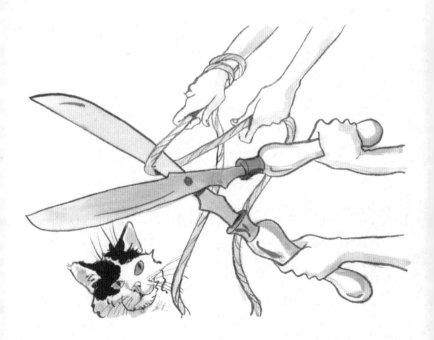

CHAPTER 3

Knot My Feet!

The girls walk out of the shed with
the stuff they've collected, back to the
hammock.

Jules "Have a seat ... and stick out
  your feet."

Rosa "My feet? What do my feet have to do with anything?"

Jules "I have to practise making a good knot so our trapeze won't fall down. Get it?"

Rosa (looking puzzled) "Not really."

Jules "Well, I have to practise tying the rope around something. Might as well be your feet. Now do you get it?"

Rosa "No, but it sounds like fun. Weird, but fun."

Rosa sits on the hammock and sticks her feet in the air. Jules ties her friend's ankles together with a big knot.

Rosa "Ouch. Are you trying to strangle me—my feet, I mean?"

Jules "Look. A perfect knot."

Rosa "It's very fancy, that's for sure. Where did you learn to tie a fancy knot like that?"

Jules "My auntie. She was in the Girl Guides. She showed me all kinds of knots. Like sailors use on boats."

Rosa "Now what?"

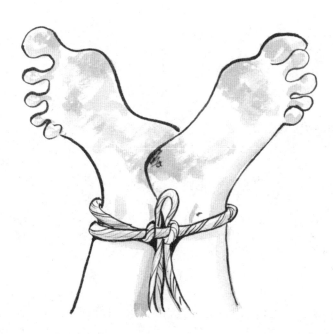

Jules "Try to walk."

Rosa "With my feet tied together?"

Jules "Yeah. It'll be fun."

Rosa (shrugging) "Help me stand up."

Jules pulls her friend out of the hammock. Rosa takes two little hops and falls over. Jules laughs.

Rosa "Okay, fun's over. Untie me, now!"

Jules pulls Rosa up, and then unties the knot by yanking on one end. Rosa falls down, again.

Rosa "I'm spending more time on the ground than flying through the air!"

Jules "Sorry, Ro. Come on. Now that we know how to tie the knots, we can build the trapeze."

CHAPTER 4

Way Up There?

Rosa hands Jules the broom.

Rosa "Tie your fancy knots."
Jules "Wait. These bristles have got
to go."

Rosa "If you insist. Give me your mum's hedge clippers."

Jules "What are you going to do?

Rosa "Give this broom a little haircut, that's what."

Using the hedge clippers, Rosa cuts the broom bristles as short as she can.

Jules "That's not much better, but I guess it'll have to do."

Rosa "Tie your super-knots so we can hang this thing up."

Jules ties a rope on each end of the stick.

Rosa "Next … we have to tie each rope to the branch."

Jules "Yeah. Be right back."

Jules runs into the shed and comes out with an old chair.

Rosa "You're climbing way up there on that wobbly old thing?"

Jules "I suppose so, if I'm tying the knots. Why? Are you scared?"

Rosa "No. It just … ummm … looks kind of high from down here."

Jules "If I can reach it standing on a chair, it's not that high. Anyway, you can't be scared of heights if you're going to be a trapeze star."

Rosa tries to hold the wobbly chair steady while Jules stands on her tiptoes to tie the ropes around the branch.

Rosa "This chair is going to fall apart any minute. Hurry up!"

Jules ties the knots quickly and jumps off the chair.

Rosa "You tied those knots really fast. Sure they're going to hold?"

Jules "Of course!"

Rosa "Okay, then me first."

CHAPTER 5

Flying Rosa-lini

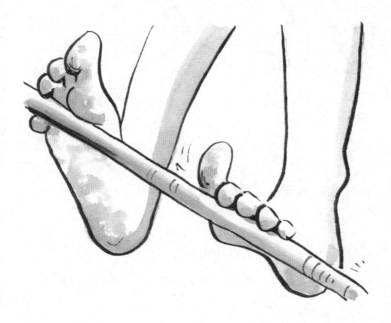

A smiling Rosa puts her feet onto the bar. With her first movement, one rope loosens and the bar falls slightly lower on one side.

Rosa "Jules, your perfect knots are not so perfect. This thing's crooked."

Jules "What are you complaining about? Your feet aren't touching the ground."

Rosa (looking down) "Yeah, there's about twenty centimetres between me and the ground."

Jules "I'm going to count to three. Then I'm pushing. Ready?"

Rosa "Stop talking and start pushing!"

Jules "One. Two. Two and a half. Two and three-quarters."

Rosa "Hurry up!"

Jules "Three!"

Jules gives her friend a big push to set the trapeze in motion.

Rosa "I'm flying."

Jules "You're a Flying Rosa-lini!"

Rosa "AAAAAArrrrrgggggghhhhh."

The knots come undone and Rosa, the bar and the ropes all fall on the ground. The girls laugh so hard that Rosa's tummy hurts and Jules's eyes get all watery.

Rosa "Your knots were hopeless!"

Jules "I think the rope broke."

Rosa "It was the stick. The stick didn't make a good trapeze bar because it thought it was still a broom."

Jules "Being a trapeze artist isn't easy. Maybe we should just be clowns."

Rosa "Yeah, because that was the greatest clown act ever."

Jules "Well, it made me laugh, anyway. Do it again!"

GIRLS ROCK!

Trapeze Lingo

Jules

Rosa

bar The part of the trapeze that you stand on, sit on or hold on to (usually a hollow metal bar).

Big Top The main tent in a circus, where the trapeze acts often take place.

catcher The person who catches you when you let go of the flying trapeze in your circus act.

leotard The skin-tight stretchy costume you wear during a trapeze act—it was invented by a guy named Léotard.

net Stretchy mesh fabric close to the ground that catches you if you fall off the trapeze.

ropes The cords or cables that hold the bar and keep it flying!

GIRLS ROCK!
Trapeze Must-dos

☆ Ask your best friend to help you choose a cute leotard for your flying trapeze act. It should be your favourite colour and have some sparkles on it.

☆ Learn how to fall correctly— especially make sure to protect your head and your back.

☆ If you fall off the trapeze when you work at the circus, make sure you fall into the net and not into a big pile of elephant poo.

☆ Make friends with the clowns. Otherwise, they might make fun of you while you're trying your moves on the trapeze at the circus.

☆ Get a good watch if you want to be successful on the flying trapeze, because it requires split-second timing to ensure that the catcher catches the flyer.

☆ Make sure your feet are always clean before you fly around on a trapeze above people's heads.

☆ If it's your turn to catch somebody, don't fall asleep on the job!

☆ Start getting information about trapeze schools if you want to learn some fancy moves on the flying trapeze.

Trapeze
Instant Info

A trapeze is a horizontal crossbar suspended by two vertical ropes.

The bar usually weighs about 2 kilograms.

The three most common forms of trapeze include:

• the flying trapeze (when you jump off a small platform and grab the bar and swing)

• the swinging trapeze (when you start swinging from a still position)

• the static trapeze (when you move around the bar while it stays still).

Most trapeze artists work for circuses.

The flying trapeze was invented by the same guy who invented the little stretchy outfit—Jules Léotard.

To be good on a trapeze, you need strength, agility and good timing.

The name "trapeze" comes from the Latin word *trapezium*, which describes the shape made by the bar and ropes. The shape has four sides including two parallel lines, represented by the ropes and is called a trapezoid.

The most famous song about trapezes is "The Daring Young Man on the Flying Trapeze", which was a huge hit way back in 1867!

GIRLS ROCK!
Think Tank

1 How much does a trapeze bar usually weigh?

2 What kind of trapeze swings and swivels?

3 If you fall off a trapeze, what should you try to protect the most?

4 Where do most trapeze artists work?

5 Who invented the stretchy, skin-tight costume that many acrobats, artists and dancers wear?

6 What do you need to build a trapeze?

7 If you fall from the trapeze while working at the circus, where should you aim?

8 What are the three most common forms of trapeze?

Answers

1   The trapeze bar usually weighs about 2 kilograms.

2   A dance trapeze swings and swivels.

3   If you fall, protect everything—but especially your head and back!

4   Most trapeze artists work at the circus.

5   Jules Léotard invented the stretchy skin-tight costume worn today by many acrobats, artists and dancers.

6   To build a trapeze, you need a bar and some rope.

7   If you fall off a trapeze while working at the circus, aim for the net (and avoid the pile of elephant poo).

8   The three most common forms of trapeze are the flying trapeze, the swinging trapeze and the static trapeze.

How did you score?

- If you got all 8 answers correct, start shopping for a really cute leotard to wear during your flying trapeze act.

- If you got 6 answers correct, ask Mum or Dad if there are any trapeze classes you might take to learn how to move on a trapeze.

- If you got fewer than 4 answers correct, maybe you can get a job selling leotards to trapeze artists (or shovelling elephant poo out of their way).

Hey Girls!

I hope you had fun reading this story. You know what I love most about reading? I can open a book and read a fantastic story about funny people or cool animals without even moving. And I can read wherever I want—in my room, in the library, in the park—anywhere. (When I was little, I tried to read in the car, but it made me feel sick. If that happens to you, ask your mum or dad about using some headphones to listen to books recorded on CDs.)

You can have even more fun if you read "Trapeze Dreams" out loud with somebody else—like your best friend or mum or dad. Here's another idea—you and your class can use this story to put on a play.

To bring the story to life, get some cool props. What would work for this story? A broom? Some rope? A wobbly chair?

Who will be Jules? Who will be Rosa? Who will be the narrator? (That's the person who reads the parts between when Jules or Rosa says something.) Maybe a talent scout will visit your class and you'll be invited to Hollywood for a movie audition. No matter what happens, you'll have fun!

You know what my dad used to tell me? Readers are leaders. So keep reading!

And, always remember—Boys may think they rule, but Girls Rock!

Holly Smith Duberg

Holly talked to Jacqueline, another *Girls Rock!* author.

Jacqueline "Did you like the circus?"

Holly "I loved the popcorn and the elephants and just about everything, except …"

Jacqueline "Except what?"

Holly "Everything except the poo smell."

Jacqueline "Did you want to be a trapeze star?"

Holly "Yeah, but not because of the fancy moves on the bar."

Jacqueline "Why, then?

Holly "I liked it when they fell off and bounced in the big net. That looked really fun."

Jacqueline "I guess you're more of a bouncer than a flier."

GIRLS ROCK!

What a Laugh!

Q What did the clown say to the trapeze star?

A You sure hang around here a lot!

GIRLS ROCK!

Read about the fun
that girls have in these
GIRLS ROCK! titles:

Birthday Party Blues
Pony Club

Doubles Trouble
Football Crazy

Dance Fever
Minigolf Face-off

Trapeze Dreams
Two at the Zoo

... and 20 more great
titles to choose from!

GIRLS ROCK! books are
available from most booksellers.
For mail order information please
call Rising Stars on 0871 47 23 010
or visit www.risingstars-uk.com

44